Gg Hh Ii Jj Kk Ll Mm

Uu Vv Ww Xx Yy Zz

Dear Parent,

The My First Steps to Reading® *series is based on a teaching activity that helps children learn to recognize letters and their sounds. The use of predictable language patterns and repetition of familiar words will also help your child build a basic sight vocabulary. Your child will enjoy watching the characters in the books place imaginative objects in "letter boxes." You and your child can even create and fill your own letter box, using stuffed animals, cut-out pictures, or other objects beginning with the same letter. The things you can do together are limited only by your imagination. Learning letters will be fun—the first important step on the road to reading.*

The Editors

All Rights Reserved. Published by Scholastic Inc., 90 Old Sherman Turnpike, Danbury, Connecticut 06810, by arrangement with The Child's World, Inc.
Scholastic offers a varied selection of children's book racks and tote bags. For details about ordering, please write to:
Scholastic At Home, 90 Old Sherman Turnpike, Danbury, CT 06810, Attention: Premium Department

Originally published as *My "g" Sound Box* by The Child's World, Inc.

My First Steps to Reading is a registered trademark of Grolier Publishing Co. Inc.
SCHOLASTIC and associated logos are trademarks and/or registered trademarks of Scholastic Inc.

ISBN 0-7172-6506-4

Printed in the U.S.A.

My "g" Book

(This book concentrates on the hard "g" sound in the story line.
Blends are included. Words beginning with the soft "g" sound
are included at the end of the book.)

written by Jane Belk Moncure
illustrated by Colin King

Little  had a box.

"I will find things that begin
with my 'g' sound," she said.

"I will put them into my sound box."

Little g opened the gate and went into the garden.

Little  found

goats

in the garden.

Did she put the goats into her box?

She did.

Then Little g found grass,

lots and lots of green grass.

She put the green grass
into the box with the goats.

But the goats ate it all up!

Little  found grapes,

lots and lots of grapes.

She put the grapes into the box.

But the goats ate up all the grapes, too!

What could Little g do?

She found a gorilla.

She put the gorilla into the box
with the goats.

Did the goats eat the gorilla? No.

The goats grinned.

The gorilla
grinned, too.

Little  found a guitar.

She played the guitar.

The gorilla danced.

Then the goats danced with the gorilla.

Everyone giggled!

Little  found some glasses.

She put the glasses on the goats.

Then she found  goggles.

She put the goggles on the gorilla.

Just then, a goose and gander walked by.

"What funny goats! What a funny gorilla!" said the goose and gander.

Little  g caught the goose and gander.

"You belong in my sound box," she said.

23

The goose got into the box all by herself.
"I will give you a gift," she said.

Then the goose laid an egg made of gold. All of it was made of gold!

Little g looked around her garden.

guitar

gate

grapes

goose

egg of gold

gander

26

"What a great group of 'g' sounds," she said.

Can you read these words

with Little  ?

glove

glass

goldfish

game

grasshopper

globe

Little  has another sound in some words. It is a soft sound.

Can you read these words?

Listen for the soft "g" sound.

gingerbread

geranium

giraffe

gerbil